THE LANGUAGE DISORDERED CHILD

A New Look at Theory and Treatment

G. M. FRASER and **J. BLOCKLEY**

Edited by **P. A. Berse**

The NFER-Nelson Publishing Company Ltd.

Published by The NFER-Nelson Publishing Company Ltd.,
Darville House, 2 Oxford Road East, Windsor, Berks. SL4 1DF.
First published, 1973
2nd Impression, 1977
Reprinted, 1982
© G. M. Fraser and J. Blockley, 1973
ISBN 85633-031-0

Printed in Great Britain by
John Gardner (Printers) Ltd., Hawthorne Road, Bootle, Merseyside L20 6JX

Text drawings by T. S. Graves

Distributed in the USA by Humanities Press Inc.,
450 Park Avenue South, New York, N.Y. 10016, USA

PREFACE

MR FRASER AND MRS BLOCKLEY present an original and highly innovative approach to the treatment of language disordered children. They have used linguistic theory and creative observation to develop a treatment which builds structurally through perception to meaningful speech.

The authors have departed radically from the behaviourist context in which much speech therapy has grown. They have attempted to combine the insights of structural linguistics with Piagetian notions of perceptual development, and have succeeded in this synthesis by taking no assumption for granted. Meaning is seen as an active achievement on the part of the child, with cognitive and perceptual antecedents which can be defined.

This collection of three papers, written over a period of two-and-a-half years, describes the evolution of a new treatment for language disordered children. Theory and treatment evolved together within the context of the day-to-day work at Braidwood Audiology Unit in south-east London. Braidwood afforded the authors the opportunity to search for and develop ideas which could be evaluated in the light of working problems; it is the creative use of the clinical setting which distinguishes the authors' use of linguistic theory. Theory has been valued not as an end in itself, but as a potential tool to be both shaped by and to probe clinical experience.

The nature of the authors' collaboration represents, in some sense, an analogue of the substance of their work. They have brought together and shared their respective skills, in the form of historical theoretical perspective and vigorous responsiveness to clinical detail, in such a way as to give life to ideas and action which add to our knowledge of language acquisition and our ability to facilitate it where it has failed to grow.

The fact that these papers are presented as points along the line of the development of treatment techniques is indicative of the attitude of mind which is central to the treatment itself, that is to say that the authors have maintained a problem-oriented approach throughout. They have attempted to use mistakes to ask further questions and to make those questions increasingly relevant to the organizing principles of language growth. In so doing, they have drawn heavily on the work of a number of philosophers, linguists, and psychologists from Kant to Piaget. The case material presented at the end of Papers One and Three illustrates how theory and practice have been allowed to inform one another over time through the maintenance of a perspective open and responsive to clinical data.

The data are the behaviour of language disordered and deaf children. In describing this behaviour and in drawing generalizations from it, the authors have tried to keep in mind the whole experience of the child's perceptual world. The treatment they have evolved is thus related to that whole experience and not to isolated bits of it. This orientation places great demands on the therapist, for it requires of him not only the specific skills of recognizing and attending to defects in language production, but an ability to imagine himself into the child's perceptual construction of the world and to respond to it appropriately.

Mr Fraser and Mrs Blockley have enabled us to see how they thought through and worked toward their current treatment techniques. Their contribution should be of interest not only to speech therapists, but to all those interested in the child's acquisition of language.

P.B.

ACKNOWLEDGEMENTS

THE AUTHORS acknowledge their indebtedness to the ILEA for the provision of necessary treatment facilities and for the support and encouragement of the Officers concerned.

Thanks are also extended to Yale University Press for permission to quote from Cassirer (1953) *The Philosophy of Symbolic Forms* Volume 1: Language; Volume III: The Phenomenology of Knowledge.

INTRODUCTION

IN 1969 the senior writer took up his duties as Educational Psychologist for Deaf and Partially Hearing Children with the Inner London Education Authority. During the subsequent three years, assessments were carried out on every deaf and partially hearing child in the Authority's special schools and units, a population of some 600 children. It is worth describing the initial reactions which this first experience of deaf education evoked in a psychologist with considerable experience of normal educational psychological practice.

There was the sobering impression that a mode of teaching concerned with oral education was failing, by a wide measure, to achieve its objectives. While there is no evidence that the adult deaf do not lead useful and rewarding lives, their social and vocational scope is constricted by limited attainment in communication and educational skills. Simpson (DES Report 1964) found that of 359 deaf and partially hearing children aged 14 or 15 and over in 36 schools for the deaf, only 80 had reasonably adequate speech. Hans Furth (1966) estimated that of 5,000 deaf children in the United States, only 10 per cent achieved a reading ability of Grade 3 standard (approximate reading age eight years).

As the primary aim of oral education of the deaf is the integration of the deaf into the society of their hearing peers, the implication of failure is the continuation of the traditional social isolation of the deaf with its consequent stigma of inferiority. The poverty of achievement in deaf education is rendered more disillusioning in that the massive contribution of physical science in the shape of the development of transistorized hearing aids appear to have left the hard core of the problem relatively untouched.

The second reaction was one of hope. No psychologist could spend any time in a deaf school without realizing the immense scope offered in deaf education for purposive research, promising dramatic insights in the fields of language, education and social psychology. The perfect control group in any study of children's language development is a group of children with no naturally acquired language. It is striking that there is an almost complete dearth of such purposive research. With the honourable exceptions of Furth, Oleron and Myklebust and the isolated studies of Vygotsky and Luria, the field of deaf education remains almost untouched by psychologists. The teacher struggling to develop oral communication in intelligent but severely deaf children may be excused a wry smile on reading of expensive University projects aimed at developing language in chimpanzees.

It became increasingly evident that unless the resources of psychology were urgently brought to bear on the problems of deaf education, the ideal of 'oralism' and its objective of successful integration of the deaf into the wider community would be diluted to the extent that the deaf would be confirmed in their traditional status as an excluded minority, condemned to relatively menial occupations and limited aspirations. This sense of urgency blended with a feeling of frustration in that the demands made on an educational psychologist specializing in audiological work in a school population of some 400,000 seemed to leave little time or energy for research. What did happen, however, was that the work itself developed by its own nature into a form of research.

The presenting symptom of children in both the deaf school and in the audiology unit is absence or retardation of speech development. This situation requires the use of solely non-verbal intelligence test material, which represents a more direct study of mental processes than material calling for the symbolic intervention of speech. As in verbal tests, stringent administrative and scoring procedures must be followed, thus ensuring objectivity. Many years' experience of intelligence testing of normal hearing children supplied the norm against which the performance of speechless children might be viewed qualitatively.

Again and again during these assessment procedures one was forcibly reminded of the words of Hans Furth:

'Perhaps it is a good thing that the presence of linguistically incompetent persons forces the behavioural scientist to study thinking without language. By this is implied not merely the necessity of employing nonverbal thinking tasks, but also a certain healthy skepticism with regard to linguistically determined notions.'   (Furth, 1966)

The writer found that 'linguistically determined notions' such as the dependence of thought on language, 'inner speech' and its relationship to the regulation of behaviour, and the verbal basis of concept formation in children, that all these came to appear facile precisely because of their linguistic determination. They failed to survive the prolonged study of the speechless deaf.

In addition, however, to these negative findings, positive evidence about the mental functioning of speechless children came from the performance of these children on non-verbal test material. In the case of both the deaf and the language disordered child[1], a certain pattern of performance emerged suggesting a link between language development and what will here be defined as 'perception'. A striking feature was the degree of similarity in the performances of deaf and language disordered children. These findings formed the starting point for further investigation, also by non-verbal testing, and for a search for an hypothesis which might explain these findings.

The papers which follow represent in their sequence the time dimension of this study in that the third paper, written a year later than the first two, takes into account the results of forms of language therapy arising from theoretical considerations set out in the earlier papers.

Finally, although this study has its origin in work with the deaf, the first application of a form of language therapy based on it was with language disordered children. Administrative factors were responsible for this—the pressing need for advising about appropriate treatment for such children who had been assessed at Braidwood, and the involvement of an experienced speech therapist interested in this work.

Above all, the theoretical work presented here and the treatment which has grown with it and from it has evolved in response to the challenge presented by Hans Furth (1966):

'The objective condition of aphasia is something which any theory of thinking and language must eventually be tested against.'

[1]The term language disordered will be used to designate a child whose hearing and speech apparatus is intact, who is of normal intelligence and in whose case no severe adverse emotional and cultural factors operate, but who has failed to develop sufficient communication ability to cope with ordinary school placement. This 'diagnosis by elimination' has subsequently been confirmed by the results of tests designed to identify perceptual disorder.

PAPER ONE   January 1971

THIS STUDY has three aspects. Its practical foundation lies in the results of diagnostic psychological tests administered in the past 18 months to approximately 500 speech deficient and speech impaired children. Most of these were either deaf or partially hearing, the rest being children with normal hearing but retarded development of speech. Theoretically it is based on a study of the literature on language from the writings of philosophers of the 18th-19th century to those of the psycholinguists of the present day. The study lastly involves the formation and trial of a programme for the development and remediation of language.

'Stimulus-response' or 'associative' theories of language gained wide acceptance during the first half of this century. Sapir (1921) has summarized the basic principle of this approach in describing language as a 'merely conventional system of sound symbols'. The fostering of the acquisition of speech and language in deaf children as well as the treatment of language disordered children have been in accord with these theories. Most existing tests of language, such as the Illinois Test of Psycholinguistic Abilities, are based on such theories.

An older tradition of philosophical speculation and enquiry about language is reflected in the writings of Wilhelm Von Humboldt, among others. Humboldt held that underlying any human language is a system that is universal that simply expresses man's unique intellectual attributes.

Noam Chomsky is regarded as an innovator in the field of research in language. To some extent this is due to the prevailing climate of behaviourist psychology in which his writings first achieved prominence. These writings are generally, however, in the rationalist tradition. Thus, he sees 'linguistic competence', the knowledge of a language, as an abstract system underlying behaviour, and the complexity of language as reflecting the deeper principles of mental organization.

It is natural that psycholinguists of this school should try to find the universals of language in rules of grammatical relationships and syntactical organization. It is difficult, however, to see in such rules the innate nature which psycholinguists claim for linguistic competence. To what extent can an abstract non-verbal system be linguistic in any meaningful way?

An alternative approach might profitably be adopted by the psycholinguist in seeking the deeper principles not primarily of language but of human mental organization and relating these to language. In order to do this, however, the 'psychic distance' from language must first be established. This can only be done satisfactorily by eliminating speech. In carrying out an extensive programme of diagnostic psychological testing of children with no speech, inadequate speech and defective speech, employing almost entirely non-verbal material and methods of administration, not only has this 'psychic distance' been achieved, but it has been possible to examine how mental organization proceeds in the absence or relative absence of speech and consequently in an abnormal language condition. From this has come a clearer understanding of normal language and its relationship to mental organization.

The inclusion of both the deaf child and the language disordered child within the scope of this study has the advantage of allowing us to compare the mental infrastructure of language in two pathologically different conditions. It is generally assumed that in the developmentally language disordered child there is a direct impairment of such infrastructure. What seems less certain is the precise nature and extent of the deaf child's disadvantage in language. Does deafness merely restrict environmental auditory stimuli or does it have other effects which are equally serious but more subtle?

Test Material

The following tests were used in the course of this study:
1. The Merrill-Palmer Scale of Mental Tests;
2. Snijders-Oomen Non-Verbal Test of Intelligence;
3. WISC Performance Scale;
4. Frostig Developmental Test of Visual Perception;
5. Illinois Test of Psycholinguistic Abilities;
6. Reynell Developmental Language Scale.

The children's performance on certain sub-tests of these Scales will be referred to in detail later on. These sub-tests are:

Snijders-Oomen Non-Verbal Test of Intelligence (SON)
(a) *Mosaics.* The child is asked to copy increasingly difficult designs with red and white square tiles.

(b) *Picture Series.* This is a test of the understanding of relations which are neither purely spatial nor completely abstract but have a concrete meaning. Cards must be placed in a series according to temporal sequence. It is the same in many respects as the WISC Picture Arrangement sub-test.

(c) *Sorting.* This is a test of sorting, involving simple categorization and concept formation.

(d) *Knox Cubes.* This test involves tapping sequences of increasing complexity of bricks set out in a row of four following demonstration by the examiner.

Developmental Test of Visual Perception (Frostig)

Spatial Relations. In this sub-test the subject is asked to copy simple line patterns by joining dots. Of the Frostig sub-tests this is the easiest to administer reliably in a non-verbal fashion.

These sub-tests will henceforth be referred to by the abbreviated titles given above.

The Evidence

In testing children without speech or with grossly inadequate or defective speech one is repeatedly struck by evidence of poor appreciation of *relationship in time.* The sub-tests which are illustrative in this respect are the Picture Series (SON), Picture Arrangement (WISC) and the Knox Cubes.

References to the difficulty experienced by the deaf child in temporal sequencing are made in two articles. Father Tervoort (1964) writes of the basic difference between a contact system based on sound and the ear and one based upon light and the eye.

'The eye is the organ of light and space, the ear is the organ of sound and succession in time.

This last difference is the most fundamental one for the distinction between the two communication systems.

Norm for the eye is the distinctive visibility of the outlined qualities and typical characteristic for the eye is the simultaneity of the perception in space and from a distance. Norm for the ear is the distinctive audibility and the typical characteristic for the ear is the succession in time of the perception as part of the perceiving person abstracted from the sounding object.

The ear is the organ for the measuring of before now and thereafter, and therefore is the organ of time and relations.'

Analysing the performance on WISC Performance sub-tests of ESN partially hearing children, Pickles (1966) reports as follows:

·'It is to be noted that the shape of the "profile" appears to be related to speech competence, in that the "profile" becomes sharper with decline in speech, and is most pronounced in the absence of speech. This occurs through the relationship which certain sub-tests appear to have with speech and language, scores on these varying directly with speech competence in the deaf. The Picture Arrangement sub-test, in this group, showed the closest relationship with speech. It was also the sub-test which correlated most highly with estimates of academic progress. Correct solutions to the problems presented in this sub-test require an appraisal of a total social situation and the arrangement of the picture to form a logical temporal sequence. It may be that the lack of language handicaps a child particularly in appreciating temporal sequential relationships; hence the difficulty experienced by such a child in this type of problem.'

The normally hearing but language disordered children assessed by the writers so far have been in the chronological age range four to seven years.[1] At this age, failure in the Picture Series and Picture Arrangement sub-tests carries little significance. On specially designed material (to be described later) at a more appropriate level of difficulty, however, these children have given convincing evidence of a disability comparable to that of the deaf. The reason for this similarity can only be a matter for speculation. Where the auditory channel, though unimpaired, contributes little in terms of meaning, it may be that the child rejects such stimuli and builds a communication system based on the eye as the deaf child does.

Secondly, the evidence of this testing programme points to a defective appreciation of *relationship in space* among deaf and language disordered children.

Far from the deaf child having the compensation of being 'good with his eyes', the evidence of this testing programme points to defective visual spatial perception as a feature inherent in the condition of congenital deafness as it appears to be in developmental disorder of language. The 'profile' which emerged from the programme of testing deaf children, using various sub-tests of the SON, showed a positive correlation between performance on sub-tests loaded with either temporal or spatial perception and progress in the development of oral communication, whereas sub-tests sampling non-verbal reasoning ability (Analogies) or categorization/concept forming ability (Sorting) were found to be in line with teachers' estimates of general innate potential.

[1]Subsequently the ages of most of the language disordered children assessed dropped to within the range two-and-a-half to five years.

Before concluding this section, it is interesting to consider the transposal mistakes which abound in the written work of deaf children (e.g. Jhon, rianing, chips and fish, etc.). It is possible to regard these as arising from a defective grasp either of spatial or temporal relations. The writers have been led to the view that a rigid distinction between spatial and temporal relations may obscure the more crucial underlying organic wholeness of the perception process. Recent work in the sub-test analysis of Frostig's Developmental Test of Visual Perception has lent support to this view.

The Theory
Sound is energy distributed in time and space (in frequency, amplitude and duration). The elements of speech have no real identity except in combination with other elements. For example, the recognition of plosive consonants can be altered by altering the following vowel. In other words, identity of these elements is established by ordering them in space and time.

Proceeding a stage further in the organization of speech, meaning is only achieved by ordering words in space and time. The richness of language is such that few single words have absolute labelling value, situation or context being necessary to endow words with even this limited function.

Lea (1970) draws attention to the manner in which children with severely retarded speech and language, when attempting to form sentences 'put their words together in much the same way as they would string beads of similar shape, size and colour—with no particular reason why one should precede or follow another'.

Immanuel Kant saw space and time as two pure 'forms' of

FIGURE 1: On the next page are shown composites of the efforts of five successively referred grossly language disordered but normally hearing children on the Spatial Relations Subtest (Frostig). Of these children, one succeeded on Design 3, two on Design 4 and none on Designs 5 and 6. Details of the age and IQ of each child are given below. The writers feel that these composites convey more clearly than the subtest age scores do the bizarre quality of the attempts of these children.

Children	Chron. Age	IQ (SON)	Sub-test Age Score
1	5·3	87	No Score
2	6·0	86	4·9
3	6·0	100	5·0
4	6·9	100	6·0
5	7·0	Above 100	4·9

	MODEL	CHILDREN'S ATTEMPTS
3		
4		
5		
6		

'sensuous intuition' (Anschauung), these forms being *a priori*, that is, not learned from experience in the course of time nor derived by inductively generalizing from particulars. In contra-distinction to the 'forms', all contents of knowledge are given through the contacts of experience—this being the material which is assimilated and understood only by virtue of the *a priori* forms of both intuition and thought.

'Nothing ever enters our ken without conforming to their combined prescription. The forms are the universal and necessary conditions of the very first appearance of anything whatsoever to human perception and furthermore of its becoming progressively intelligible to our understanding. The forms are thus *"constitutive"* of our whole experience of the world.'

(Cassirer, 1953a)

This use of the word 'constitutive' evokes comparison with the transformational process by which the surface structure or phonological component of language is related to deep structure (or semantic component) in the psycholinguistic analysis of language.

This interpretation avoids the impasse created by the postulation of linguistic syntactical rules (by which the child relates sound and meaning) which presents us with the problem of how either the rules or the meaning can precede the other.

One practical implication of our acceptance of Kant's thesis would be to accept in the case of the deaf child not only the restriction of auditory input, but also the impairment of this 'sensuous intuition' which in turn functions to 'constitute' the material supplied by the auditory among other channels.

Furthermore, since this impairment would seem to be an impairment not of sensory experience but of intuition, the child's deprivation cannot be compensated for merely by increasing sensory experience in the course of the auditory training young deaf children receive. Before the stimuli supplied by such increased sensory experience can be 'constituted', remedial measures must first be brought to bear on the 'forms' which enable such 'constitution' to take place. This would, moreover, apply equally in the case of the language disordered child.

Speech can be defined as energy which is distributed in a complex manner in space and time. It constitutes an object of perception in the same way as distributions of matter such as physical objects in the child's environment. Furthermore, speech and language obey the principle of categorical or conceptual form, which Kant regarded as a pure form of understanding, intuitive in origin.

'Traditional logic tells us that the concept arises "through abstraction": it instructs us to form a concept by comparing similar things or percepts and abstracting their "common characteristics". That the contents of comparison have specific "characteristics" that they possess qualitative properties according to which we can divide them into classes, genera, species, is usually taken as a self-evident premise, requiring no special mention. And yet this seemingly self-evident premise embodies one of the most difficult problems of concept formation. First of all, the old question arises as to whether the "characteristics" according to which we divide things into classes, are given us prior to language formation or whether they are supplied only by language formation.'

(Cassirer, 1953a)

Roger Brown's child 'Adam' (1958), for example, was able at the age of two years to manipulate without error in his speech, three categories of words—nouns, verbs and modifiers. It would be difficult to see this ability as arising from abstraction from the analysis of sensory data in the case of the child of this age any more than his creative efforts in language can be ascribed to a power of analogy.

~ Further investigation is required of the ability of deaf and language disordered children to categorize and form simple concepts. Some of the most grossly language disordered children assessed showed quite satisfactory competence in this skill and there seems little evidence from the standardization of the Sorting sub-test (SON) of a general disability in deaf children in this respect. It is planned, however, to pursue this investigation by including this Sorting sub-test in future assessments of these children. It is understandable that, according to Kant's thesis, the deaf child should be defective in the 'sensuous intuitions' of space and time but intact in the 'intellectual intuition' of categorical and conceptual form. If, however, it is found that the language disordered child exhibits the same pattern, the question then arises of whether language disorder may not also be a condition of sensory deprivation, but of a type not measurable or describable in terms of auditory acuity.

The rest of this paper concerns the formulation of a training programme for the development and remediation of language based upon these interpretations of the basic principles of language and the administration of such a programme to a young language disordered child.

Considerable experience of work with severely handicapped children (autistic, cerebral palsied, language disordered and intellectually sub-normal) had caused the speech therapist to become dissatisfied with traditional methods of language therapy involving language stimulation techniques, behaviour shaping and conditioning aimed at improving comprehension. This dissatisfaction stemmed not only from the meagre results obtained, but also from the belief that such therapy concerned itself too much with elements of language rather than with the relationships between them—with parts rather than with wholes.

Further, traditional speech therapy seemed to operate at too advanced a level. If a child does not comprehend speech, then the stage *before* speech must be investigated. In language therapy, diagnosis is proved correct only by the immediate success attending *each stage* of the therapy and by the accelerating progress.

The aim of the programme at Braidwood was to develop the child's appreciation of relationship in time and space and his ability to categorize and to form simple concepts. Since it seemed difficult to see how the language disordered child's difficulties could be remedied using the medium in which his disorder lay, non-verbal material only was used and the presentation of this material was carried out largely in non-verbal fashion.

The Assessment and Treatment of Simon[1]

Simon was first seen in June, 1969 at the age of four years 10 months. Hearing was normal. Speech was unintelligible—no consonants were heard and he was using only three word phrases. His IQ on the SON was 67 and his vocabulary level on the Peabody PVT was two years six months. No other assessment of speech and language was possible at that time, as the clinic was new and most of the equipment had not arrived. No speech therapist being available, he was referred to a local clinic for intensive speech therapy. He received a month of articulation work, mainly on initial plosives, with little result. His speech therapist left and he was referred back to Braidwood for speech therapy.

Simon's scores on the Renfrew Action Picture Test were far below the lowest norms for four-year-olds. He could not be tested on the Renfrew Articulation Test, but a detailed phonemic assessment showed that consonants were either omitted or replaced by /n/ a nasal plosive, or clicks. He had one or two correct sounds in specific words—e.g. *b*all, *mummy, c*at, and he used /s/ and /t/ once or twice incorrectly in a final position. He could imitate all consonants in isolation for /dz/ and /r/. He had little spontaneous speech, consisting of either single words or two word combinations, as far as it was possible to determine at all.

Work began on improving articulation, mainly to gain the co-operation of the parents, who were extremely worried about this

[1]The names of the children whose treatment is described in these papers have been changed in order to preserve their anonymity.

aspect. They had been trying to teach 'b--all', k--ey', 'd--oor', etc. with little result. The only success had been with the word 'ball'. They were resistant to a change in methods of treatment and it took some weeks to gain their co-operation. Simon worked on all sounds at once—they came in final positions at first, then medially and then initially. He worked hard and improved quickly. The Reynell Developmental Scales arrived at Braidwood in November and Simon showed a Comprehension level of three years 10 months. The Expressive Scale could not be administered because of his unintelligible speech.

A school visit was made. The headmistress felt that Simon was not suitable for normal school—he could neither recognize his name, nor trace it, couldn't look after his dinner money and couldn't find his sister's class. He never spoke. The school was prepared to give him a chance until Christmas.

In January 1970 he was talking more spontaneously but with bizarre constructions—'scissors in there, else scissors in there'. He started to come three times a week instead of twice as his parents were less busy after Christmas. The school had put him forward for a statutory examination as an educationally subnormal child. He was re-tested on the Peabody PVT to compare his score with that of six months earlier. He had a level of three years three months, an improvement of nine months. Most of his correct responses were nouns; there were very few verbs.

He was tested on the Merrill Palmer with a resulting Mental Age of four years nine months, IQ 85. His score on the Reynell Developmental Language Scale (Verbal Comprehension) was in line with this result—an improvement of 12 months in three months. His Expressive Language was only at a three year level. His score on the Renfrew Articulation Test was 43 per cent; although he had improved a good deal, he was still not easily intelligible.

All Simon's words were labels—there were few action words and so therapy concentrated on increasing expressive language by working on sentence construction. He found this extremely difficult. He learned the actual action words very quickly but could not learn the structure. He would say 'girl running' and later would say 'that girl running'. He had little idea of word order in sentences and might say 'That boy sitting—is'. He would freely interchange small words like 'with', 'on', 'a', 'the' and had no idea of rules of tense or plurals. However, Simon liked to do well and worked very hard to learn the sentence pattern appropriate to a particular picture. He did not generalize this knowledge and could not invent sentences of his own to communicate things which were important to him, but if shown a picture he would begin automatically with 'That boy is . . .' in a very stilted and unnatural fashion. During this time, at Easter 1970, he was admitted to a school for delicate children near Braidwood so that he could have daily speech therapy and be a member of a smaller class. He liked the new school and quickly settled in, but his language remained stilted and unnatural, although he had a few spontaneous comments such as 'us got a flat'.

Simon had, therefore, made considerable progress. His articulation had improved from almost no consonants to a score of 64 per cent on the Renfrew Articulation Test. His language had apparently improved so that his Comprehension was at a comparable level with his mental age, and his Expressive Language appeared to be at a level of five years one month. But he was not talking like a five-year-old. He could describe some of the pictures in the Content section of the Reynell Test, but only by substituting relevant words in the sentence patterns he had learned. For example, he would say, 'That boy is carrying some bread for the mum'. 'That girl and boy is carrying some washing for their mum.' 'That boy and girl is laying the table for the mum.' Although he could describe pictures in this way, he could not *use* language and could not generate new sentences. Therefore, in June 1970, age five years 10 months, Simon was completely reassessed. His IQ on the SON was 80, mental age five years. He showed particular difficulty with the Mosaic and Arrangement tests. Because of the former difficulty, the Frostig Test of Visual Perception was given. Simon co-operated very well on this test, but showed difficulties in every sub-test ranging from three years six months for Form Constancy and three years nine months for Figure Ground, to five years three months for Eye Motor Co-ordination.

The Illinois Test of Psycholinguistic Abilities was given and he showed the difficulties typical of a language disordered child. His scores on each sub-test varied considerably, ranging from two years 10 months (Auditory Memory) to five years nine months (Visual Association). The results did not give an indication of the type of language remedial programme which would help Simon. He had already been coached in sentence construction, auditory discrimination and all the conventional speech therapy language treatment, but new words he acquired were still poorly articulated, and he could not really make use of what he had been taught. Results from the SON and Frostig showed that Simon's sense of space and time were considerably undeveloped. It was felt that a programme aimed at developing these senses would provide Simon with what was missing and he would consequently improve his language more naturally.

The programme began in mid-September.

Treatment

Simon had already been attending the unit for speech therapy every day for an hour, and this was not changed. Part of the time was now used in investigating *relationship in space* and using ideas from the Frostig Programme for the Devlopment of Visual Perception, and part of the time devoted to devising exercises for investigating and developing Simon's ability to appreciate *relationships in time.*

Sorting

Simon's ability to sort and categorize was good. He could classify toys into groups—putting together all the baby's things, all the animals, all the things his mother used. Since he had no obvious difficulty here, exercises designed specifically to help him in this area were not included.

Relationship in Space

Since we had no idea at this time how to begin to link evolving theory to practical treatment, the Frostig Programme for the Development of Visual Perception was used as a basis from which to develop treatment. This consists of a set of work sheets based on Frostig's five areas of visual perception used in her test, together with a teacher's guide which contains useful ideas for exercises in each area, using three-dimensional materials prior to the pencil and paper exercises. Since working with Simon much of this programme has been abandoned, particularly with younger children, but it served as a useful structure on which to base treatment. At that time these exercises were only used with three-dimensional material as Simon was not ready for the pencil and paper exercises (as in the area of Spatial Relations, where he had no idea how to do even the easiest work sheet). Using his Frostig test results, work began with the section on Form Constancy where he had shown his greatest difficulty.

He did the pencil and paper exercises as well as the earlier exercises suggested in the Teacher's Guide.

The pencil and paper exercises for Figure/Ground were not available, so work concentrated on the other four aspects. He did some of the Eye-motor Co-ordination work sheets, but most of the work was done with Section 3—Form Constancy, where he had performed most poorly on the test. The pencil and paper exercises were done as well as shape puzzle boxes, making patterns with simple shapes when more than one picture was required, sorting different shapes, etc. Simon enjoyed these and worked well. After three to four weeks of this, work on Position in Space and Spatial Relations was introduced. He found the former quite easy, but was not able to do the pencil and paper exercises of the latter. Preliminary work was done—copying patterns in a peg board, making three-dimensional brick patterns to resemble two-dimensional drawings, etc.

Relationship in Time

Simon could not put pictures of a story in the correct order, so very simple ones were made.

FIGURE 2

Simon would watch a brick being placed in the middle of the table, moved to the edge and knocked to the floor. He could repeat the actions but could not put the pictures in the correct sequence. Therefore, simpler temporal exercises were devised.

Simon could identify noise making toys when his eyes were closed and could point to them afterwards. If more than one was sounded he could pick them out, but not in the correct order. He could pick out the appropriate picture of a ball when the noise was made under the table, but was likely to make mistakes when more than one picture was presented. He could not always copy a sequence of two coloured bricks in a cardboard tube. The bricks were dropped in the therapist's tube, for example, a red one followed by a yellow one, and Simon was expected to put a red, then a yellow brick in his tube. Once the brick was in it could not be seen, therefore this was a temporal exercise as no spatial clues were given. The tubes could then be lifted and the two sequences compared. Simon could not always see when he was wrong. If he had used the same colours he considered he was right—he did not realize the order was different. We worked on both these exercises, using both visual and auditory temporal sequencing. With the latter, Simon had to listen to the sound sequence, then put out the pictures of the sound makers in the correct order, then listen to the sequence again and say if he was right, or correct his mistakes. Another exercise was introduced involving visual and auditory channels—copying a sequence of brick tapping.

He improved quite quickly in all three exercises and once he could copy a sequence of three fairly reliably, the story sequence was re-introduced. He now had no difficulty with the pictures of the brick on the table nor with other things which had been demonstrated first

He showed more difficulty with sequences like that in Figure 3,

FIGURE 3

and they had to be discussed. After this he might reverse them, but he soon achieved insight. More difficult sequences were introduced such as a jug filling a glass, which he at first confused with the one above. He had no difficulty with the following sequence (Figure 4),

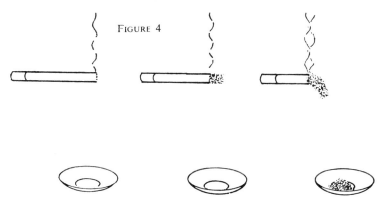

FIGURE 4

but had to talk about it before he could do it. More difficult exercises were introduced until he could use the ESA 'Look and Find the Story' pictures, which were about his age level.

While this programme was going on, Simon's speech was improving as well as his sense of time. He began to remember what he had had for breakfast or lunch the day before. On Monday he could describe what he had done on Saturday and Sunday and began to realize that on Friday he would be away from school for the next two days. He began to volunteer more information and said that on Guy Fawkes night 'me did pull my hat over eyes—might go blind'.

He still used bizarre sentences such as 'Ours cousin did gave me that' but by December was saying 'I did it' instead of 'me did it'. He still couldn't say 'Let's', 'it's or 'didn't' but said 'It is' or 'I did not'. He was reassessed in mid-December and on the RDLS showed comprehension of six years and Expressive Language above six. His age was six years four months. His sentences in the Content section were far more normal. 'The Daddy's digging' and 'The little girl put the apples in the mud'; 'The little boy and the little girl's carrying something and the woman and man come—can see some shops, and fish and cheese.' He was much more interested in doing the test and when he saw a penny amongst the toys in one section, he said 'I would nick that penny'. One of the dolls sat precariously and he said 'That one would fall over in a minute—I do think so—look—is bending'.

Reassessment on the SON, ITPA and Frostig showed a great improvement in the two months since the programme had begun. Simon was still in need of some help on two sections of the Frostig— Figure/Ground and Spatial Relations, and could have benefited from further speech therapy in order to correct some of his strange sentences, such as 'I do found it'. However, at the end of this three months of treatment he was able to return to normal school.

Summary of Test Results
Snijders-Oomen Non-Verbal Intelligence Scale (P-Scale)

| Date | Chron. Age | Mosaics | SUB-TEST AGE SCORES | | | |
			Picture Memory	Arrangement	Analogies	IQ
25/ 6/70	5·9	4·6	5·6	4·9	5·3	80
10/12/70	6·3	5·6	5·6	6·3	5·3	87

It is worth noting that Simon's improvement on the second assessment was due to his improved scores on Mosaics (involving visual spatial perception) and on Arrangement (involving temporal sequencing).

Frostig Developmental Test of Visual Perception

		3/7/70 CA 5·10	10/12/70 CA 6·3
1.	Eye Motor Co-ordination	5·3	6·9
2.	Figure Ground	3·9	4·6
3.	Form Constancy	3·6	6·9
4.	Position in Space	4·0	6·3
5.	Spatial Relations	4·0	5·6
	Perceptual Quotient	76	96

FIGURE 5

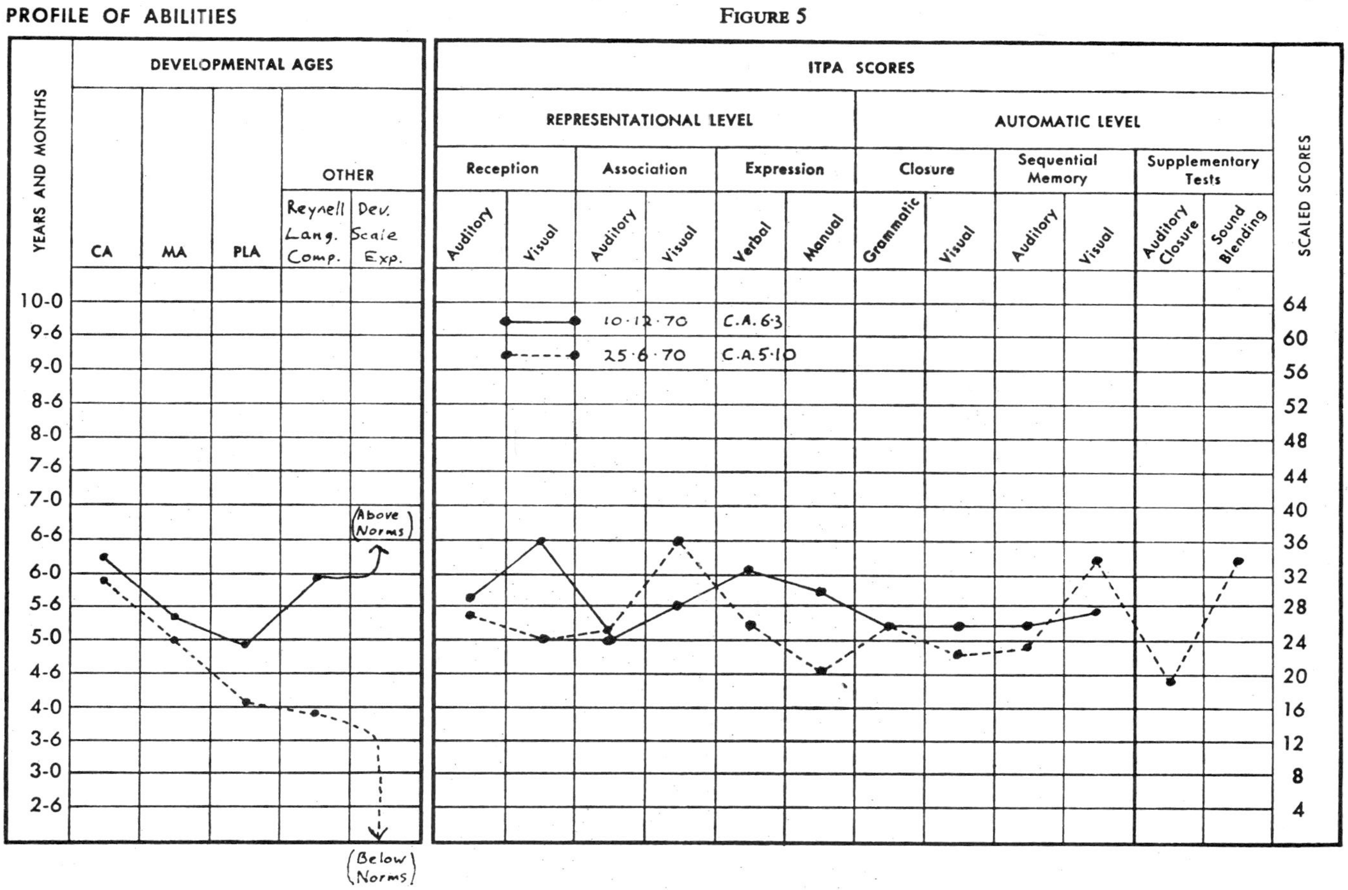
PROFILE OF ABILITIES
DEVELOPMENTAL AGES
YEARS AND MONTHS
CA
MA
PLA
OTHER
Reynell Lang. Comp.
Dev. Scale Exp.
(Above Norms)
(Below Norms)
10-0
9-6
9-0
8-6
8-0
7-6
7-0
6-6
6-0
5-6
5-0
4-6
4-0
3-6
3-0
2-6
ITPA SCORES
REPRESENTATIONAL LEVEL
AUTOMATIC LEVEL
Reception
Association
Expression
Closure
Sequential Memory
Supplementary Tests
Auditory
Visual
Auditory
Visual
Verbal
Manual
Grammatic
Visual
Auditory
Visual
Auditory Closure
Sound Blending
10·12·70 C.A. 6·3
25·6·70 C.A. 5·10
SCALED SCORES
64
60
56
52
48
44
40
36
32
28
24
20
16
12
8
4

Comments

An anomaly in this study is the use of tests based on stimulus-response or associative theories of language to assess progress brought about by a programme of language development based on a radically different theory of language. The Illinois Test of Psycholinguistic Abilities is the outstanding instance of this. In the December reassessment, the growing naturalness of Simon's language actually penalized him on his ITPA performance, e.g.

The thief is stealing the jewels.
These are jewels that he...............?
Simon   ....   nicked
Here is a child. Here are three...............?
Simon   ....   kids

Both these responses had to be scored as failure but this can be seen as a shortcoming of the test rather than of the subject's competence in language. Because of this, analysis in depth of Simon's progress was felt to be preferable to a mere quoting of test scores. It is encouraging to note, however, that even on the Verbal Expression Sub-test of the ITPA, Simon's age score increased from three years 10 months in July to five years four months in December, a gain of 18 months.

Conclusion

The writers feel that a non-verbal programme for the development and remediation of language based on the theory that the remedying of the child's perceptual disorder enables him to relate the surface structure of speech to the deep structure, thus bringing about comprehension, offers a new approach to the problem of the treatment of young deaf and language disordered children. This paper has set out no more than a hypothesis, but the acknowledgement of the inadequacy of stimulus response or associative theories of language makes alternative hypotheses necessary.

On the one hand, the 'teaching' of language is being undertaken with deaf and with language disordered children in a pragmatic manner with the emphasis heavily on technique and methodology. What is disturbing about this approach is that implied in it is the assumption that it is sufficient to know the physiological and neurological organs involved in speech.

'The development of language is complex. There is much that is not known about the failure of children to develop the ability to communicate through language. It is not necessary to wait, however, until unequivocal knowledge is available concerning the nature of the factors underlying disorders of language in order to proceed with appropriate education.'

(McGinnis, Kleffner & Goldstein, 1956)

In fact, underlying this approach is the assumption that 'language is what it seems' . . . a conventional system of phonetic symbols. Inevitably, this leads to a method of teaching language which depends on the storing, recall and association, by constant repetition and training, of a set of conventional sound patterns. Such a method takes little account of recent studies of normal language acquisition or of the growing awareness of workers in this field of the awesome complexity of the phenomenon of language.

The writings of psycholinguists, on the other hand, have issued in little of significant practical value, so far, to the teacher or therapist. It is difficult to say to what extent the lack of balance between theoretical and practical inquiry, is due to the difficulty of approaching the problems of language via speech.

If the oral education of the deaf child and the remedial treatment of the developmentally language disordered child are to be rendered effective, the methods employed must surely be grounded on a knowledge of the nature of language. The first step towards this is for the two halves of the world of language study to be brought together in order that theory and practice may fertilize and inform one another.

The present ferment of inquiry about language has the disadvantage that being essentially a reaction against behaviourist psychology it has been infected to some extent by the narrow vision of the behaviourists. To regain perspective it is sufficient to recall the words of Wilhelm Von Humboldt on language:

'We must free ourselves completely from the idea that it can be separated from what it designates, as for example the name of a man from his person, and that like a conventional cipher it is a product of reflection and agreement or in any sense the work of man (as we tend to think of concepts in common experience), not to say the work of the individual. Like a true, inexplicable wonder, it bursts forth from the mouth of a nation, and no less amazingly, though this is repeated every day and indifferently overlooked, it springs from the babble of every child; it is the most radiant sign and certain proof that man does not possess an intrinsically separate individuality, that I and Thou are not merely complementary concepts, but that if we could go back to the point of separation, they would prove to be truly identical, that in this sense there are no spheres of individuality, from the weak, helpless, perishable individual down to the primeval clan of mankind, because otherwise all understanding would be eternally impossible.'

                                                    (Von Humboldt)

IN THE FIRST PAPER an attempt was made to deduce the basic principles of language from the study of the responses of deaf and language disordered children to a variety of non-verbal psychological test items, relating these responses to what has been written about the nature of language by psycholinguists and by philosophers. It was hypothesized that these basic principles of language are threefold—relationship in time, relationship in space and conceptual form. It is proposed in this paper to investigate in greater depth the third of these principles, using the same methods of inquiry, and, since conceptual form must be regarded as being of the essence of language, to try in conclusion to reach some tentative definition of the nature of language itself.

Conceptual form is seen as a pure form of understanding, intuitive in origin rather than as arrived at by a process of abstraction from experience.

'If the concept is to bring out the common factor in a series of particulars, it must have them as distinct sensuous or intuitive realities, before it can stamp them with its own form.'

(Cassirer, 1953b)

In other words, before the child can form a concept of 'dog' the series of creatures whose common characteristics he will abstract must already be in some way limited and defined by intuition.

Of these three hypothesized principles of language, the concepts of relationship in time and space are described by Immanuel Kant as 'sensuous intuitions' (Anschauung). The implication of this is that this intuitive act takes place as soon as sensory life begins at birth. On the other hand, conceptual form, although intuitive, must be regarded as subject to maturation and experience and to correlate to some degree with intelligence.

The first paper discussed the necessity for establishing the 'psychic distance' from language of which Noam Chomsky has written. The study of language solely by discussion and introspection is made almost impossible by the inevitable confusion between 'language' and 'speech' and the consequent difficulty in particular of defining exactly what 'the name' of an entity really is. In the investigation of the mental functioning of the profoundly deaf and of the grossly language disordered child using non-verbal intelligence test material, the complete or relative absence of natural meaningful speech makes possible the direct study of language. By separating at the outset in this way the phenomenon of language from its natural medium of speech we start by calling into question the most widely accepted definition of the nature of language, by J. B. Carroll (1964), 'a socially institutionalized sign system'.

The real criticism of this 'nominalist' position rests on a philosophical rather than a linguistic study of language. Philosophers through the ages have approached language with the reverence appropriate to one of the fundamental mysteries of the human mind. For Wilhelm Von Humboldt this 'true inexplicable wonder' could in no sense be 'a product of reflection and agreement or in any sense the work of man'. With the writings of Noam Chomsky and others in the past 20 years language has regained the status of a proper subject for philosophical inquiry destined to lead us into the ultimate depths of humanity—a status which as 'a merely conventional system of sound symbols' it could never claim.

Until progress has been made towards resolving this issue of the nature of language, the educational treatment of the deaf child and of the language disordered child will be at best an ineffective process of trial and error.

The Card Sorting sub-test of the Snijders-Oomen Non-Verbal Intelligence Scale is a non-verbal test of categorization and of concept formation. The examiner sorts his materials according to a certain category and the subject must then discover the principle underlying the sorting and apply it to his materials. This is demonstrated (Figure 6) with eight cards, four with triangles and four with circles on them, which the examiner sorts. The subject is then given another eight cards, four of which have triangles and four having circles depicted on them.

The procedure is demonstrated and corrected where necessary. In the rest of the card sets the subject's cards bear different shapes and objects from the examiner's but these obey the same sorting categories as the examiner's. For example, (Figure 7) the examiner sorts eight squares into large and small ones and the subject has to sort eight moons into large and small ones. The 11 trials have the following criteria or categories for sorting, covering a mental age range of from six to 15 years:

Figure 6

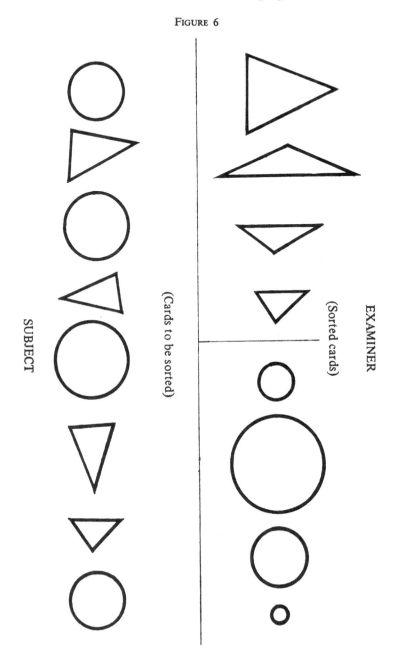

FIGURE 7

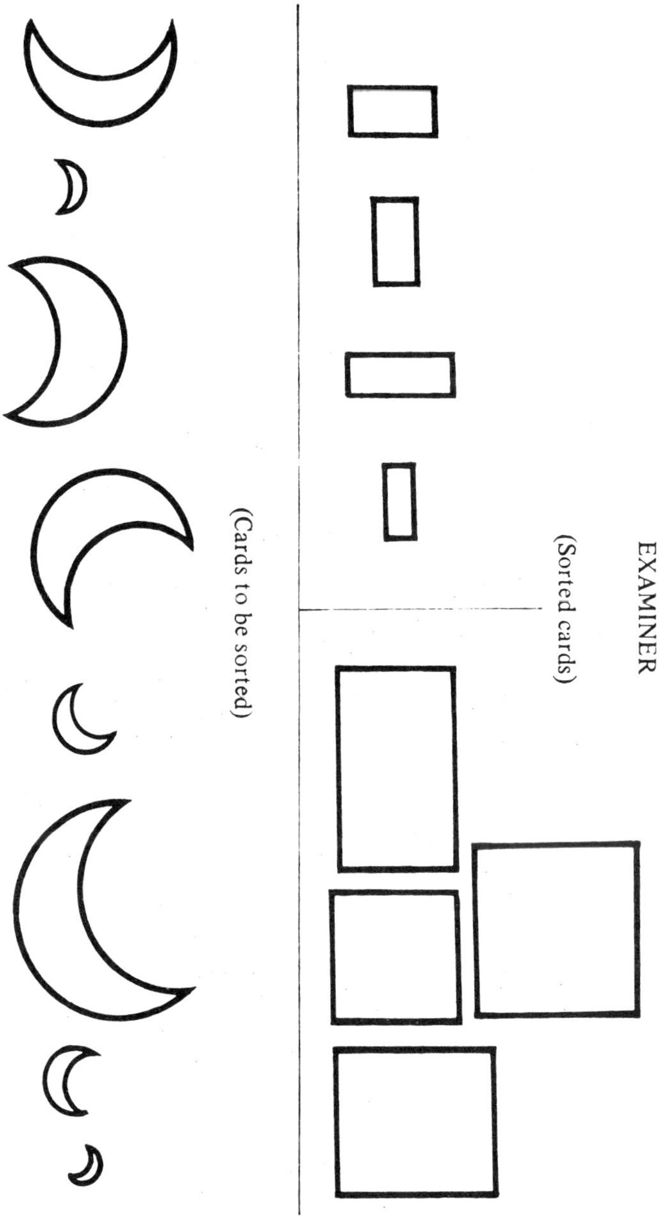

SUBJECT

(Cards to be sorted)

(Sorted cards)

EXAMINER

1. Singles—trebles   6. Agreeable—disagreeable
2. Large—small   7. Wood—metal
3. With cross—without cross   8. Young—old
4. Open figures—closed figures   9. Similar—dissimilar
5. Angular—circular   10. Living—not living
                        11. Opposite—not opposite

This sub-test has been standardized on both deaf and hearing children. The norms for deaf children are the same as for the hearing until the fourth item above is reached, when a discrepancy in favour of the hearing child appears which reaches two years of mental age at the most difficult items. The material and procedure are designed for completely non-verbal presentation.

What mental process is involved in the correct performance of each item? The subject is presented with the problems as in Figure 1.

To respond correctly the subject must form a concept of the figures on each group of four cards, that is to say, a concept of triangularity and of circularity (although he may form only one and thereby exclude the other cards) by which he can form two corresponding groups of four cards from those he is given.

If the concept involved in successful performance is not a visual perception and is not a verbalization, then what is it? The theory that a mental image is involved ignores the fact that categorization and concept formation apply equally to actions, attributes and abstract qualities as well as to objects.

If the concept of 'animal' is something which possesses sufficient flexibility to include *all* animals and yet to be no particular animal; if the concept of colour is something which includes all colours but is no one colour; if the concept of symmetry includes every possible example of symmetry but is no one such example; then the only conceivable definition is that it is in fact a *name*—although not, of course, a verbal one.

Is the non-verbal name a novel idea? In fact, such a theory has considerable status in the history of philosophical thought.

'The more resolutely the character of the concept as a pure relational texture is worked out in modern logic, the more sharply the inference tends to be drawn that over against the ideal meaning of this structure the name remains something secondary and external. "A concept", writes Burkamp, for example, "is a relational structure that can be related to an indeterminate manifold. For our thinking this concept becomes a unity and in important cases is designated by a name. The name, the word, however, is no more the concept than my name is myself. The name is something external to the concept and has nothing to do

with its essence. . . . If I understand a new mechanical contrivance, it is a concept for me, even if I do not give it a name. The functional relation, transferable to an indeterminate manifold, is the concept. The name is a convenient appendage. It serves primarily as a badge and means of expression for the concept."
An "abbreviation" of this kind can—it would appear—claim no independent value, no antonomy. Its function is solely one of substitution, and all knowledge must at some time learn to dispense with such representation and confront things themselves in their pure being. It becomes knowledge in the strict sense only insofar as it succeeds in doing this—insofar as it casts off the covering in which language and the word threaten to obscure it.'

(Cassirer, 1953b)

The first theory which must be considered as alternative to the 'nominalist' one, is that a concept is a name which is inherent in members of categories, which is in fact as much a part of these members as their appearance, colour, motion and texture, and that conceptual form consists in the intuitive assimilation (subject to maturation and intelligence) of such a name.

This brings to mind Roger Brown's quotation from Plato's Dialogue 'Cratylus',

'Hermogenes: I should explain to you, Socrates, that our friend Cratylus has been arguing about names; he says that they are natural and not conventional; not a portion of the human voice which men agree to use; but that there is a truth or correctness in them, which is the same for Hellenes as barbarians.'

(Brown, 1958)

Such a theory, while going some way to explain the performance of speechless deaf children on concept formation tasks, takes no account of, and violates the essential principle of Piaget's persuasive theory of cognition, namely that:

'To become a meaningful object, a thing to which one reacts, the organization of the organism must be capable of adapting to it in a twofold direction: by assimilating the thing into its organization and by accommodating the organization to the particular characteristics of the thing.'

(Furth, 1966)

In other words, the concept is the product of a creative interaction between percipient and perceived, not the passive assimilation of aspects of the external world.

The use of the sorting sub-test of the SON with the deaf child can be extended imaginatively as a potent instrument of inquiry and research. At the end of the standardized sub-test, the child will readily sort any eight cards into two groups of four, a sufficient number to render correct performance as being beyond chance. For example, Michael, a deaf child of eight years who is without speech or comprehension of speech,[1] could sort without error four illustrations of modern objects from four of old-fashioned objects taken from a booklet called 'Post Office Through the Ages'.

In this way the speechless deaf child can be shown to possess abstract concepts as well as concrete ones. Furthermore, following Hans Furth, one can use this technique to determine whether concepts are true ones or 'pseudo-concepts' (to use Furth's term). Furth's example of a 'pseudo-concept' is that of an 'opposite' (e.g. *rough* as the opposite of *smooth*). Another identified by the writer is that of 'colour' as against black/white.

Study of the 'non-verbal name' brings realization of the pitiful inadequacy of such an appellation. Once again the attempt to verbalize leads to confusion. In fact this entity is truly indescribable in nature, though not in function.

For the sake of clarity the non-verbal name described above will be referred to in this paper as the 'nomen', since 'name' has a verbal connotation. The 'nomen' must be understood as referring to a category. For example, no deaf child could sort correctly four photographs of men called Smith from four of men called Jones.

The 'nomen' then refers to categories or concepts. It is, however, bound to categories, to restrictive sensuous conditions and is therefore an unsatisfactory medium of thought and before it can *become* a satisfactory medium of thought it must free itself from this bondage.

'The word of language differs from the sensuous, intuitive image precisely in that it is no longer weighted down, so to speak, with a sensuous matter of its own. Considered in its mere sensuous content it appears volatile and indeterminate, a mere breath of air. But from the standpoint of the pure representative function precisely this intangible, ephemeral quality is also the basis of its superiority over the immediate, sensuous contents. For the word, one might say, no longer possesses any independent, self-subsistent mass which might offer resistance to the energy of relational thinking.

(Cassirer, 1953b)

[1]Michael was assessed (by a hospital consultant) as a hearing but ineducable child at three-and-a-half years and spent three years in a Training Centre without amplification or auditory training until he was found to be deaf and placed in a partial hearing unit. He has made little progress towards speech and has no lip reading ability. He is of average intelligence.

The moment of liberation therefore is the moment when the nomen becomes the word. This is the celebrated moment when Helen Keller apprehended from Anne Mansfield Sullivan, her teacher, her first word—'water'. Following this breakthrough in linguistic understanding Helen Keller in her own words 'was able to think three times as quickly as before'. Not, it is important to note, that she was now able to think for the first time, but by achieving the conversion from nomina to words, her thinking had been released from its bondage to perception and intuition.

What is the nature of the relationship between the nomen and the word? Precisely this, that the word is the nomen endowed with energy, the projection of the nomen. The nomen is lifeless, a reflection of what is; the energized nomen is the word and this energy is the life which endows language with its creative generative power. Prehistoric man's first grunt was the beginning of this process of energization.

'The process of dematerialization and detachment continue; the sign tears itself free from the sphere of things, in order to become a purely relational and ordinal sign. Now it is no longer directed toward any single thing which it aims to "represent" directly, to set before the mind's eye in its intuitive contours. It aims rather to mark out a universal, a determination of form and structure which is manifested in the individual example but can never be exhausted in it.'

(Cassirer, 1953b)

The role of metaphor in endowing language with its generative power is dealt with in Roger Brown's book *Words and Things* (Chapter IV). It is in metaphor that both the process of liberation from restrictive sensuous conditions and the energy of relational thought are most evident.

Of crucial importance to our understanding of language are the relative roles played by perception and by conceptual or categorical form. Conceptual form is a pure intuitive form of understanding whose medium is perception. The liberation of language from sensuous restrictions occurs in speech, which involves the appreciation of relationships in time and space. So at every level in the development of language perception is involved. Conceptual form, however, while a basic principle of language, is a form which must be worked through and outgrown if language is to develop creative generative power. Of these two principles, therefore, perceptual form must be regarded as more basic to the development of language than conceptual form.

Animal perception has been shown to be inferior to human

perception in that 'it does not yield stable things with determinate attributes which may change in the thing itself but also possess an intrinsic property of permanence . . . so that the world is not yet homogeneous and constant in our sense' (Roger Brown, 1958). If, therefore, the chimpanzee who excels the feeble minded child in problem solving ability is yet inferior to the latter in the ability to develop language, this inferiority must be seen as a perceptual rather than an intellectual inferiority.

If language is not a 'conventional system of sound symbols' which man has developed to express and communicate thought, how can it be defined? Language is neither perception nor conceptual form but issues inevitably from the interaction of these, a form, as it were, of combustion where these elements are present. Language begins with this 'combustion' and includes everything which occurs as a result of it up to and including speech.

In conclusion, two important points must here be reiterated, one concerning the theory of language, one concerning practical issues.

In the first place, although the purely behaviourist explanation of language is now widely regarded as untenable, the methodology of study appropriate to simulus-response theory persists. Is the nature of language to be discovered by analysing language into elements such as memory and studying each by laboratory-type experiments (using, for example, digit or nonsense syllable recall tests) the essence of which is that they are divorced from the meaning of language? Since Chomsky and others have demonstrated that it is the deep structure of language that carries meaning, how can meaningful language be fostered by repetitive training in the manipulation of surface structure which represents merely the phonological component?

A more fruitful approach must surely lie in seeking the basic unifying principles of knowledge, the principles which lie at the meeting place of sound and meaning.

'For Kant, form is a mere expression of relation, but for this very reason, since all our knowledge of phenomena ultimately dissolves into a knowledge of temporal and spatial relations, it constitutes the truly objectifying principle of knowledge.'

(Cassirer, 1953a)

In the second place, with children who lack speech or who suffer from disorder of language, how are we to approach the educational problems involved? If the child can hear but not comprehend speech, is it reasonable that the medium of remedial education should be the one in which his disability lies? Can a disorder of language be remedied by repetitive practice in the *medium* of language?

Again, the deaf child is by definition a sense-perceptually impaired child. If language has as one of its basic principles the perception of forms in space and time, it is superficial to see the problems of deafness merely as those of inadequate auditory input. It would be regrettable if the ideal of successful oral education of the deaf were to be given up as unattainable for all but a minority, because the subtle but pervasive side effects of deafness were not properly understood, if the problem were seen as merely the amplification of auditory input when the mental structure to 'constitute' that input, to integrate it and make it meaningful is defective because of the child's perceptual impairment.

The deep structure of language which carries the semantic component is a *mental structure* the nature and dimensions of which have been discussed in the first paper. It is in the question of the existence of mental structure that the study of language leads us to take issue with the basic tenet of behaviourist psychology. Brain damage lies outside the field of the educator and therapist; mind damage (more precisely, the impairment of mental structure) does not.

What has been styled the 'rationalist' theory of language which this study supports, offers at once a more demanding challenge to the educator and therapist but one containing more prognostic confidence and hope.

PAPER THREE June 1972

A FURTHER YEAR'S WORK with deaf and with language disordered children has elapsed since the writing of the Second Paper. In all, some 1200 children with no speech or with defective comprehension of or expression by speech have now been assessed. Nothing has emerged from the assessment or from the treatment of these children to call in to question the validity of the hypothesis set out in the first two papers.

Hans Furth (1966) regarded as an open question 'whether aphasia should be considered a specific linguistic deficiency or a general cognitive defect to which verbal behaviour is most sensitive'. The conclusion drawn by the writers is that the second alternative is the valid one, although for 'cognitive' the writers would substitute 'perceptual' (regarding perception as the basis of cognition). Secondly, although the validity of non-verbal language therapy must be established in due course by satisfying objective criteria, the results of such therapy over the past year have been wholly encouraging.

What this further year's work *has* contributed has been deeper insight into the nature and complexity of the perceptual process and into the nature of the relationship between perception and speech.

Speech is one physical phenomenon among many in the child's environment. In the process of coming into command of his environment, the child learns to assign meaning to the sensory stimuli which assault him from all sides, by selection and by 'constitution' (Paper One). Perception is this assigning of meaning to sensory stimuli or (to employ psycholinguistic terms) the relating of deep structure to surface structure. In order to establish the 'physic distance' from speech, it may be helpful to regard the receptor organ of speech, the basilar membrane, in the same light as the other sense receptors (the retina, nasal membrane, epidermis and tongue surface, etc.). How, then, does the physical phenomenon of speech differ from other physical phenomena in the child's environment—his mother, the table, the smell of food? One difference can be seen as a varying degree of complexity of the relationship (in space and time) of the elements composing these phenomena. The most complex in regard

to such relationship is speech, which has none of the stability in time
and space of the other phenomena cited. Although speech can in this
way be seen as a physical phenomenon in the environment of all
living creatures, its perception and reproduction is the property only
of human young and to a large measure accounts for man's biological superiority.

One of the advantages of daily work with the deaf is that it confers
the ability to imagine a society without speech. Whatever intriguing
features such a society might have, it would not be the society of
homo sapiens, of culture, science and philosophy. Speech is not in
fact the 'best show man puts on'; it is the criterion of his sapience.
Seen from this viewpoint the development of speech and of the
comprehension of speech is not something which cognitive development makes possible, is not an 'object of knowing', it is itself a stage
in cognition. Conversely, every Piagetian stage in cognitive development is a stage in the development of speech. Speech is as integral a
part of human development as erect posture and digital opposition
are of the development of the higher species. It necessitates the same
developmental prerequisites—innate potential, relevant experience
and maturational factors.

'It seems more in accordance with the facts though less simple, to
suppose that the co-ordination of sensorimotor schemes, which
are actively built up during the first 18 months of life, starting from
hereditary reflexes, is a necessary condition for language acquisition to become possible.'

(Sinclair-de-Zwart, 1969)

Piaget states that the child has a 'schema' of 'chair' when he is able
to make an appropriate response to a chair. Put another way, the
child is able to relate the surface physical structure of the chair to the
deep structure of 'chair', the 'structure of knowing' to use Piaget's
phrase. The child must 'transform the thing (chair) into an object of
action and of knowing.' This transformation is a complex process
depending, for example, on the previous development of the appreciation of the permanence of objects. More than this, the child must
have learnt to see consistency amid inconsistency, to relate the
thousand conflicting and changing sensory impressions of the chair
to a stable known entity to which he can make his appropriate
response.

Similarly, the child has a 'schema' of speech when he can transform
the elliptical ungrammatical colloquial utterances of his parents into
'objects of knowing', into the 'kernal sentences' which obey the
universal rules of language and which carry meaning. But to quote
Kant again, 'all our knowledge of phenomena ultimately dissolves

into a knowledge of temporal and spatial relations' (Cassirer, 1953a). Perception is therefore the assigning of meaning to the physical phenomena in the child's environment and this is brought about through the child's appreciation of the relationship in time and space of the elements of such phenomena.

The second two of the following three passages of free composition (by a seven-year-old normal child, a ten-year-old profoundly deaf child and a 15-year-old aphasic child) illustrate perceptual disorder in relation to language.

(a) 'When I grow up I would like to be a teacher because you get lots of money. So that I can be rice and I allways wanted to be one because I like to teach children and I some times I play it at home and I want the children to be big like 12 or 13 some thinks like that Because I do not like to shout All the time and big girls dont make a nouse.'

(b) 'Jane that you the man. Jane walked to home. Jane bag a lot of potatoes. Jane frighered. Barking a dog. Jane dropping a potatoes. The road a potatoes. The car squash a potatoes. Jane cry was a sad. The squash a potatoes. The broken and bag. Jane cry picked up a broken. Jane broken a bag. Jane went to home. Jane went to bed and cry.'

(c) 'All we will go to the Summer Holidays. I am going to live Southsea on Side Sea. This will go to shining. I am going to swim have out cold. I am going to walk or look had at hot sunny. all we will be an ice cream cold. I am going to out in box eat orange or tea cup. all poodle. Rev it cat brone. I will go to my on Side Sea all poodle to the bus live Portsmouth. We will be play like the ball, they will go by Sat like. all we are going watch television. I am going to wink out on Dad. all we will be to the Summer Holidays.'[1]

An interesting point is that distortions such as in (b) are characterized as 'deafisms', while the distortions in (c) are ascribed directly to brain lesions in discrete areas of the cortex, but the writer of (b) suffered no brain damage while that of (c) is not deaf. In both these examples the transformation from deep structure to surface structure is grossly defective owing to the writer's disordered appreciation of temporal and spatial relationships. Thus, although the pathologies are different there is a common intermediate factor or condition, namely perceptual disorder, at which effective treatment must be directed.

An advantage of a comprehensive and coherent theory of perception is that such a theory can embrace otherwise baffling pathological disabilities such as 'dyslexia'. In this condition the child is unable to

[1]C is quoted from Lea, J. (1970) *The Colour Pattern Scheme. A Method of Remedial Language Teaching.*

earn to read, to transform the surface structure of what he reads to deep structure, although spoken language may be unaffected.[2]

Perceptual development follows a biological and hierarchical sequence in which more basic and grosser modalities employing contact receptors (e.g. tactile perception) support the development of more complex and more sophisticated modalities (e.g. visual perception) which employ distance receptors. Another hierarchical factor is the stability in space and time of the elements of phenomena perceived in the child's environment. The most complex and biologically most significant modality is auditory perception. This is really a combination of modalities involving both contact reception (air pressure on the tympanum) and distance reception (localization of stimulus). To a greater degree than the visual modality, auditory perception works through symbolism and in this way liberates thought from its bondage to physical phenomena—to the world of the senses.

Since, however, auditory perception, like a sixth sense, depends for its development on the normal function of biologically less complex ones, the source of any disorder of the former must be sought in the latter. The assessment and treatment of the language disordered child must therefore concentrate on the functioning of the primary perceptual process which in normalcy provides the foundation for the development of the more complex perceptual processes on which the comprehension of and expression by speech depends.

Further Treatment Notes, September 1972

Reviewing the treatment of Simon after an interval of a year's further work with language disordered children, fresh insights into perceptual processes and their relationship to the development of speech have caused the remedial programme to be broadened and its emphasis altered. Its aim, however, remains the same, namely, to develop the child's appreciation of the relationship of elements in his environment in space and time.

While further practical experience with children of five and six years old, more seriously disordered than Simon, has produced more exercises of the type described in Paper One, improved assessment techniques have enabled us to identify and explore disorders of perception more thoroughly by going back further in the child's biological and cognitive development to investigate perceptual

[2]Professor Meredith of Leeds University has apparently established a link between reading disability and accident proneness in children based on the hypothesis that 'Dyslexia represents a disorder in a child's perception of space, time and distance.' The Manchester Guardian, 7 June 1972.

processes involving primarily the contact receptors. Piaget's writings have been invaluable in developing methods of assessing and treating at this primary perceptual level.

Treatment by seating children at a table manipulating small material does not provide the necessary experience to overcome problems of perceptual disorder. Many feel secure sitting at the table, but their perceptual difficulties become evident when they move about the room. They have difficulty walking round the room and avoiding. obstacles—either walking into them or giving them too wide a berth. They have problems getting on and off a chair, crawling under the table, opening doors, jumping off a low step, climbing up and down stairs, or walking down a slight incline.

It is more apparent in work with very young children (CA two-and-a-half to three-and-a-half years) than with the six-year-olds that perception is a single whole entity, a unity, rather than an amalgam of several modalities or 'channels'. Words such as 'auditory', 'tactile', 'spatial' merely describe aspects of a total perceptual process and can be misleading if they are taken to represent identifiable discrete elements in such an amalgam.

The human infant perceives the world around him with skin and muscle as well as through eye and ear and on such early perceptual experiences are founded the later more sophisticated and biologically more significant ones.

The principles outlined above have been applied to a group of language disordered children, aged two-and-a-half to four, admitted to the handicapped nursery class in a school in the vicinity of Braidwood. They were diagnosed as being language disordered by our criteria and showed severe perceptual difficulties. The treatment of two boys in this group, brothers John and Peter will be considered. When first assessed, John was three years six months with language comprehension at the 11-month level—he understood 'Where's Mummy' and a few single words and recognized his brother's name. His brother at age two years five months had a similar level of language development. They used one or two recognizable words and conversed with each other in jargon. They did not use gesture or facial expression for communication and could not play with symbolic toys or show any understanding of the representational nature of toys like cars. Their performance on the non-verbal items of the Merrill Palmer Scale was virtually identical, which resulted in Peter having an IQ of 79 and John, being a year older, one of 69. However, their general behaviour was unlike that of ESN children— they were toilet trained, relatively self-reliant in dressing, etc., and were fairly mature in response. Their relationship with their mother was a close one. She realized the severity of their problem and was anxious to help them. They also had a good relationship with their father. Both parents talked to the children, took them out, and apparently provided adequate affection and stimulation. Deprivation or emotional disorder were excluded.

At first the boys attended the clinic for therapy. They were very active and would rush round the room, making exaggerated movements to avoid obstacles and often falling over. They enjoyed coming and after a few sessions John would smile when he came into the therapist's room—Peter was never seen to smile or use any facial expression. They would rush in and examine the equipment produced and would carry out the tasks unsuccessfully but too quickly for it to be possible to give help or use the equipment to gain insight into their difficulties. They could not be seen separately as they needed either mother in the room or each other. If they wanted to go to the toilet they would pull their trousers down and walk to the door—they had no other way of communicating.

The boys were coming twice a week, and with such severe handicaps this was worse than useless. Fortunately, they were given places in the nursery class for all handicaps except the deaf (which have their own nursery classes), next to Braidwood. They attended all day, five days a week, stayed for lunch and were brought from their home and returned by school bus. The class has a nursery teacher, a nursery nurse and an attendant. The teacher was experienced with all kinds of handicaps. She accepted readily the principles of such a non-verbal programme aimed at developing perception at the primary level.

The Programme is not the usual kind of rigid set of activities set out in well defined sequence and small steps that is usually prepared for language deficient children. We do not know enough about the normal development of perception to be able to devise a programme, let alone how it would apply in the case of the perceptually disordered child. However, with such disordered children some form of structure is necessary, since they function so poorly in an unstructured environment. Therefore, the day was divided by the teacher. During the first hour the children needed to settle and were allowed to choose from big toy activities—apparatus work, bicycles and the usual nursery sand, water and Wendy House activities. After mid-morning break they would sit down at tables and were given Montessori apparatus and other table top perceptual training. At the end of the morning there might be music and movement, or some dancing. The afternoon showed a similar pattern but without the visits from the music or dancing teacher. One morning a week they went swimming in the school's own pool.

The speech therapist spends one morning a week in the class, concentrating on the group of six to eight language disordered children and sees them individually or in pairs in her room once more during the week.

Peter was longer settling in than John, as he was rather young to leave his mother. However, he had a close relationship with his brother which helped him overcome any initial distress. At first, at the beginning of the morning John and Peter would ride round and round on tricycles. They showed no original ideas in play, nor did they mix with the other children. They would play with sand and water briefly but had no interest in painting or junk modelling. On the PE apparatus (a bench hooked at either end to the rungs of two PE stools) they showed no originality and had to be shown how to climb up the rungs of the stool, over the top, along the bench and down the other stool. They could not walk up the sloping bench to the top of the stool, nor down it. Peter was unable to walk down the incline from the toilets and often fell, although he was a sturdy child —he seemed to be incapable of judging the rate of the slope and the extra distance his feet would need to go. Playing with a ball, whatever size, was far too difficult and they were given a ball suspended from the ceiling at first which they could more easily control.

After break they sat at tables for individual perceptual work. Both were given apparatus to help 'motor' perception—e.g. bead threading, putting clothes pegs on the edges of a box, using the single bend, square bend and spiral bend Abbatt threading toys. John improved at these more quickly than his brother whose initial difficulties were much greater. They were both poor at putting shapes in post boxes and were given the very simple ones to do. They were also poor at sorting different shaped objects by colour. Attention was very limited with both boys and they found it difficult to sit still for long. Any task given to them had to be brief. Peter, the younger boy, was interested in sound; banging different things with a stick to compare the noises. He was less interested in the music period.

The music teacher devised a programme for these children based on the information given by the speech therapist—that they could not understand speech and were distressed by it, that sound was not very meaningful and that they were poor at imitating actions. Each child was given a drum and had to copy the teacher banging with one or two hands, quickly or slowly, loudly or softly, to a tune she sang to set the rhythm. Other movements were involved such as clapping hands, banging the drum or the floor with the stick, tapping toes, etc. At first single movements only were used and as the children progressed sequences of two movements were introduced. Peter would pay attention for a while but did not attempt to join in. John would become tense and distressed: he found imitating body and arm movements very hard and he would have to get up and leave the group from time to time. The music teacher came twice a week and after a few sessions John's need to leave the group waned and he could stay for the full 20 minutes.

After a month the boys were showing progress. They were able to climb the apparatus without help and could imitate what other children did—for example, jumping off the bench. They were able to take part in a more organized game—waiting for their names to be called before they jumped. Concentration was increasing and they were improving at colour sorting. John was beginning to do water play, but Peter's favourite activity was still riding round and round on a tricycle. After another month-and-a-half their mother reported that they were beginning to understand what was said to them and using speech themselves at home. John was hitting the ball on the string again and again with a bat and improving his aim. Sorting by colour was more efficient and he was imitating the movements better in music. He was beginning to talk to the other children in jargon. Peter had improved in all directions but he had been so bad before that he still needed to work with bead threading, threading toys, pegs, puzzle boxes and colour sorting. He was beginning to use the bat and ball and showing symbolic play with cars. He was babbling a good deal with great enjoyment and joining in the music, singing 'la la' all the time. He was also able to cope with all the people in the room. This used to disturb him before.

Three months after admission to the class they were reassessed at CA four years one month and three years respectively. Peter at three years was too young for the Snijders Oomen and was reassessed on the Merrill Palmer non-verbal items. His IQ had increased to 90— Mental Age two years nine months. His comprehension of language on the Reynell Scale was one year five months, and expressive language one year 11 months.

John was old enough for the Snijders Oomen—a more reliable non-verbal test and one which provides useful diagnostic information in language disordered children. His IQ had also risen to the 90s which confirmed our original opinion that he was not a retarded child in spite of his earlier poor test performance. His comprehension and use of language was at the two-and-a-half year level.

In the class they were using the apparatus—jumping off the higher bench and rolling over the mat, walking or sliding down the slanting bench, crawling on their stomachs under a very low bench.

John was playing with the sound toys—drums, cymbals and tambourines. He had improved with the threading toys and was doing more complicated sorting exercises. He and his brother invented their own games of hitting the ball on the string, each in turn.

Peter was still clumsy with the bead threading and other threading toys but had improved a good deal. He would also play with the sound toys and was showing much more facial expression—laughing and smiling. He was still distractable and found it difficult to pay attention to colour sorting tasks. They were beginning to work as part of a group in the music session, concentrating more on the teacher. Neither child was able to build a tower or nest a simple grading toy such as cubes or beakers. During the following month attempts were made to introduce exercises which were more geared to appreciation of temporal relationships. The brick in tube exercise which had been used with Simon (Paper 1) was now used as a test. John could only copy a sequence of two bricks of the same colour. Peter could not do the test at all. None of the 'temporal' exercises devised for Simon were suitable at this primary level of perception. The large drum and cymbal were set up on their stands and the children encouraged to hit first one, then the other in a rhythm. They were ready for this—both children had shown that they could perform exercises where they had to shift attention fairly rapidly from one thing to another. It was possible to look at all the activities in the class and to highlight the temporal element—for example, on the apparatus they had to follow a definite sequence rather than climbing it in a haphazard fashion. Another way of emphasizing order was to make them queue for the apparatus, or for throwing a ball at skittles, then fetching the ball, picking up the skittles and handing the ball to the next in the queue.

A three week Easter holiday followed, and it was encouraging to see them return showing improvement gained during the break. They began investigating new toys, kicking balls, junk modelling and painting. They were beginning to play like normal nursery age children—experimenting with toys, and beginning to assert themselves and fight for their toys. They started playing in the Wendy House with the other children and playing the piano. Concentration had improved. John was able to do more complicated shape puzzle boxes, learning from his errors. He was beginning to sort for colour, then sort each colour pile into the correct shape. He was showing some insight into nesting toys. Peter was beginning to investigate the nesting cup toys but needed help to recognize his errors.

Both boys were beginning to play with doll's furniture. They were

also walking along the low wall in the playground and jumping off.
They were now able to sit on a small chair and lean down to pick
up the bricks from the floor from all directions. They could also
stand in a hoop and lean down without shifting their feet or falling
over, to pick up toys and hand them to the therapist.

After another month they were using a good deal of language.
John: 'Patrick, no, don't touch my tractor' and 'Please do me up'.
Peter: 'Carolyn, no stop it', 'I can't find it', 'Mrs. B., can I play
with the horse?'.

Their faces were much more expressive and they no longer used
jargon. They joined in music and were beginning to sing songs like
'Skip to my loo' and 'Tommy Thumb'. Both boys were able to
stand when it was their turn and sing an approximation to 'Here I
am, Here I am, How do you do'. It was now possible to test Peter
on the brick in tube test. After initial practice he could put one the
same colour in but not two. When the sequence was two bricks he
just filled his tube to the top.

The following month both boys were choosing to bang the drum
and cymbal in turn, and they marched in rhythm when someone else
was playing them. They were able to jump into a hoop with two feet,
then into the next hoop again with two feet, but they could not skip
from one to the other without putting a foot to the floor in between.
Climbing through a vertically held hoop was more difficult, particularly for Peter.

Both boys found 'Hunt the Thimble' using a large knitted toy,
very difficult. They could not close their eyes for very long. John was
better than Peter at finding the toy.

By the end of the term John had made considerable progress with
shape puzzles, grading toys of all kinds. He was good at discriminat-
ing by touch and matching an object in his hand which he could not
see, to one of a group on the table. Peter was not so good.

During the summer holidays the boys attended a play group run
by the nursery teacher and speech therapist two days a week for
four weeks. They went on four outings. At the seaside John found
the vastness of the sand and sea a little overwhelming. He liked the
sea for a short time but would suddenly panic and have to be shown
how to turn round to get back to the sand. Peter had no such trouble.
Prior to this, careful watch was kept on him on such outings because
of his poor location of sound. But this had improved and, at the seaside, when he was called he turned to the source of sound every time.

At Crystal Palace Park they showed no fear of the animals and
each had a pony ride. They went there in the speech therapist's car
and were able to give their parents a coherent account of the outing.

They brought their lunch each day and coped very well. John could not break the paper of his chocolate bar and said: 'Mrs. B., I can't do this, it's too heavy for me.' At Windsor Safari Park, Peter saw the rhinoceros and asked its name. When he heard the name his face lit up and he said 'Lubly'.

When they were shown the photographs of the outings, John did not understand what they were, but Peter recognized the people immediately.

After the holiday they were assessed again. John, at age four years nine months, still showed an IQ of 90 on the Snijders Oomen, mental age five years,[3] and his sub-test scores ranged from four years for mosaics to six years for Picture Memory. On the Reynell Scales he showed Comprehension of three years three months and expressive language of three years 10 months.

Peter was tested on the Snijders Oomen. He was three years seven months old. His mental age was three years three months, IQ 90. His sub-test scores varied from two years nine months to three years six months. His comprehension of language was two years nine months on the Reynell Scales, expressive language was three years one month. He could copy a sequence of two bricks in a tube if they were the same colour, but not two of different colours. When shown a picture of a toy, and asked to find the toy in a basket while its picture was out of sight, he was successful 14 times and made only three errors.

More Recent Developments, April 1973

Since their last reassessment the boys have continued to progress. During the Autumn term of 1972 their natural, spontaneous language increased so that it was possible to have interesting conversations with them.

For example—John: 'Mrs. T., what's for dinner? Salad?
I don't like tomatoes.'
and   'I haven't aeroplane on my towel'.
(Why not?)
'Mrs. T. can't find it'.
Peter: 'Miss K, my mum's got a new bed.'
'My daddy's in bed. He's got a bad cold.'
'He won't put his clothes on.'
'Mrs. B., Martin hit John.'

During this term the speech therapist had developed her ideas

---

[3]In assessing children with the SON the IQ is obtained independently from the mental age.

further for treatment at the primary perceptual level. It had been difficult to investigate the tactile aspect of perception. The children did not find it particularly difficult to match small objects by touch— e.g. a teaspoon, matchbox, bead, rolled up tape measure, etc., and no subsequent line of investigation suggested itself. Reading Piaget and Woodward on the early development of behaviour and perception in the baby, certain ideas were formed as to how to explore these primary perceptual processes.

Piaget shows how a child uses tactile and visual exploration of an object in order to achieve the concept of the permanence of objects. One child sat in its pram bringing an object close to the eyes and then moving it away—repeating the action with intense visual concentration. Once the child can fix his gaze on the object he is holding he manipulates it in every way, looking intently.

Therefore, a number of baby toys were ordered—different shapes, sizes and textures, some silent, some making a noise. Pictures were made and coloured and they were the same size as the objects. Different exercises were used with these toys—at first the children were encouraged to feel, look and listen to the toy and then to match it to the picture. Some of the toys could be set out on the table and a duplicate of one toy placed in the child's hands under the table out of sight. The child would have to point to, or pick up the correct toy. These toys have provided one of the answers to the difficulties of investigating primary perception. It is possible to see if the child can match the shape but not the texture—for example, when he picks out the woolly pompon instead of the perspex ball. Some children confuse shape and others ignore relative size. Several toys can be put in a drawstring bag and a duplicate of one shown to the child. He must feel in the bag for its double without using visual clues. Complete tactile matching can be done by having each set of toys in a bag with one hand in one, and the other hand in the other bag. The child must bring out two of the same at once with no visual clues to help such as seeing one toy first or seeing a picture. All these exercises can be administered non-verbally by the therapist demonstrating to the child.

The toys are also useful for other perceptual exercises. They can be placed in fairly prominent places round the room for the child to find them. Some of them make quiet noises and can be used with the child who is apprehensive of noise.

Other ways of exploring primary perception are with equipment like a large fibreglass barrel open at both ends, or a cloth covered tunnel. Obstacle courses can be devised encouraging the child to go under, through, over or around. These activities can be presented in a structured way for the child showing severe difficulties, or the child who is improving can be observed as he becomes more accurate.

During the Autumn term these activities were carried out with John and Peter. At the end of the term, John was five and becoming too old for the nursery. He was not yet ready for normal school but was dominating Peter. He was moved into the infants' class for a term and was very proud of himself. He no longer came to the speech therapist's group, but another therapist working temporarily at Braidwood arranged to treat him for an hour twice a week.

His main areas of difficulty were planning an activity in advance, temporal sequencing, and the idea of himself spatially related to other objects and the relationships between objects. The therapist worked with him on three dimensional spatial exercises and temporal sequencing exercises in the same way as was done with Simon in Paper 1. This work continued until his reassessment at the end of March.

John's IQ on the Snijders Oomen at age five years three months was 94. His mental age was five years two months and there was only a three month discrepancy between the sub-test scores. On the Reynell Scales his comprehension was four years two months and Expressive Language four years six months. He was also tested on the Renfrew Action Picture Test—his scores here ranged from five-and-a-half to six years. The discrepancies in scoring can be attributed to his poor auditory attention. Also, his vocabulary had not improved in the term since he left the nursery. However, the even scoring on the intelligence test shows that his perceptual disorder has been virtually overcome, and he will start at an ordinary school next term. The speech therapist will assess progress after his first term. He should cope well in a big school—he is friendly and talkative and is using mature sentences, such as: 'I wasn't here yesterday because I wasn't well'.

Peter shows difficulties in attention and temporal sequencing similar to and slightly greater than his brother. Whenever possible he is given extra sessions at Braidwood to help overcome this. His physical difficulties in exercises such as climbing through hoops are lessening. He will play football with the other children. His language is improving steadily and he will often volunteer news about home. Sentence structure is maturing—for example,

'My mummy didn't come.'
'Don't throw that at me.'
'Mrs. B., will I see you tomorrow?'

At the time of writing Peter is four years and two months; if he continues to make progress he should be ready for normal school at five years. These two brothers are only representative of a number of children with severe language and perceptual disorders who are being treated by this method and who are making satisfactory progress. Each child treated in this way is adding to the diagnostic and therapeutic information available to us. Although it is still not possible to lay down a rigid programme of treatment, there are several important points underlying the therapeutic approach to these children.

1. It is non-verbal. By this we mean that we do not treat through the defective medium. If the child understands and uses some language at, for example, the level of a two-and-a-half-year-old, we use his language to encourage him in his work. If we find that our speech distresses him or distracts him from the task in hand, all treatment can be carried out non-verbally by demonstration. The treatment situation is highly structured for such children so that if the activity is at the suitable level for the child, he usually understands what is required of him.

2. It is geared to the level where the child is succeeding; but because perception is disordered, rather than delayed, it is necessary to explore all areas of perception, and to begin by investigating the primary perceptual processes.

3. Where possible we aim for errorless learning. It is possible to have children as young as two-and-a-half working with the speech therapist for a full hour. Obviously, different tasks are supplied during that time, but a normal child of the same age would not stay working for that length of time. By placing the language disordered child in a situation where he is succeeding we gain co-operation. Outside the clinic he experiences failure more than other children—he cannot make sense of what he sees or hears, nor can he understand his mother or other children. Most of these children like coming to work.

4. Treatment should be full time with an experienced nursery teacher and daily individual work with the speech therapist. Many severely disordered children come to the clinic twice or thrice weekly for help, but the best results are obtained from the children who are in the full time nursery class.

5. Treatment is complete when the perceptual disorder has been successfully treated rather than when language is up to mental level. Minor perceptual difficulties can usually be overcome in school and normal experience will improve vocabulary - and language structure in the perceptually whole child.

Conclusion

The evidence of each day's work with deaf and with language disordered children has brought the writers closer to the concept of 'Piagetian psycholinguistics'—a phrase used by Sinclair-de-Zwart (1969).

'The Piagetian psycholinguist would always try to study language as part of the symbolic function within the frame of the total cognitive activity of the child rather than as an autonomous "object of knowing".'

It seems appropriate in concluding this study of language to discuss briefly the wider implications of such a concept.

One of the difficulties attending clinical assessments of speech retarded children is the significant proportion of such children who exhibit none of the usual pathological conditions (deafness, mental retardation, gross personality disorder, etc.) which might be regarded as causative. It is customary in such cases for the retardation to be attributed to 'minimal cerebral dysfunction'.

Any such assessment, however, based on a theory of language as an integral part of human cognitive activity and development, rather than as an 'object of knowing', would of necessity include an investigation of conative and motivational factors which psychologists recognize as basic to cognitive processes.

It is the writers' experience that this added dimension renders the assessment more effective in that it brings under examination the whole child and his 'life style' rather than testing the functional efficiency of various organs in an eliminative sequence. Furthermore, a consideration of these factors must form an integral part of any programme of remedial therapy.

Secondly, if language is seen as an integral part of cognitive activity and development, then present tests of linguistic skills used in clinical assessment must be regarded as descriptive rather than diagnostic. To supplement these, comprehensive assessment procedure must be developed to investigate the functioning of the perceptual processes from which, in normalcy, linguistic skills develop. Similarly, a comprehensive and systematic programme of therapy must be devised, aimed at repairing disorders of the perceptual process in order that comprehension and use of speech may develop normally.

Thirdly, it is the contention of the writers that deeper insight into the complex relationship between language and thought than we at present possess is more likely to come from intensive and wide-ranging research with, and intelligent observation of deaf children than from any other source. The American psychologist, Edna Levine, spelt out the challenge in these words:

'For the psychologist there can be no more unique "experiment in nature" than is presented by those born deaf. Here in the midst of our highly complex culture they are living reminders of the state of man in pre-history before language was ever evolved.

They stand forth as individuals in whom mental, social and even emotional growth are achieved largely through artificial means. They might be said to represent the forced cultivation of human personality.

Countless questions come to mind regarding the impact of deafness upon basic psychic forces. How, for example, are inner drives regulated in the absence of hearing and language? How controlled? How does conscience evolve? How are compromises effected between inner drives toward gratification and the restriction of social censure and mores? What of ethical and moral values that are perforce "artificially" engendered? Through what uncharted course does personality evolve?'

(Levine, 1956)

Today, almost 20 years later, we are no nearer to answering these questions. Are these, in fact, the relevant questions? May it not be the hearing child, exposed auditorily from infancy to the influences and pressures of parents, teachers, and the mass media, who represents the 'forced cultivation of the human personality'?

At present such questions, the answers to which would surely push back the boundaries of our knowledge of the nature of the phenomenon of language, appear to lie in a 'no-man's land' between the provinces of psychology and philosophy. Why should the psychologist, however, allow a short-sighted insistence on quantification and objective measurement to deny him access to such fruitful fields of inquiry?

Noam Chomsky makes a relevant comment on the definition and scope of psychology:

'We live, after all, in the age of "behavioural science", not of "the science of mind". I do not want to read too much into a terminological innovation, but I think that there is some significance in the ease and willingness with which modern thinking about man and society accepts the designation "behavioural science". No sane person has ever doubted that behaviour provides much of the evidence for this study—all of the evidence, if we interpret "behaviour" in a sufficiently loose sense. But the term "behavioural science" suggests a not-so-subtle shift of emphasis toward the the evidence itself and away from the deeper underlying principles and abstract mental structure that might be illuminated by the evidence of behaviour.'   (Chomsky, 1968)

Psycholinguistics similarly at present takes the form of a 'science of behaviour'—of verbal behaviour. The disadvantage of this is a serious one—that it excludes consideration of the 'deeper underlying principles and abstract structures' which underlie and give meaning to verbal behaviour. It is salutory once more to recall the balance maintained by Von Humboldt between the 'dry mechanical analysis of the physical aspect of language' on the one hand, and the 'philosophy of language destined to lead us into the ultimate depths of humanity' on the other; the one giving meaning and impetus to the other.

There seems little prospect of fruitful psychological work in a field of inquiry arbitrarily restricted by the acceptance of the basic premise that language is a 'socially institutionalized sign system' and the results of educational and therapeutic treatment of deaf and language disordered children based on this premise throw corroborating doubt on its practical validity.

It is recognized that if the existence of mind, and consequently of 'deep underlying principles and abstract structures' is denied, then the field of study is reduced automatically to that of 'verbal behaviour'. One must consider the possibility at this point that our lack of impressive progress in gaining insight into the nature of the phenomenon of language in recent years has been due to the fact that enquirers have set out from psychological and linguistic positions which have prevented them from viewing the phenomenon in its entirety. No better guides can be recommended for this purpose than the study of deaf and language disordered children.

Only an approach of the type characterized by an emphasis on 'Piagetian psycholinguistics' seems to concede to language the integral part in the biological development of the child which its role in the progress of Mankind would appear to demand.

BIBLIOGRAPHY

BROWN, R. (1958). *Words and Things*. New York: Free Press.

CARROLL, J. B. (1964). *Language and Thought*. EnglewoodCliffs, N.J.: Prentice Hall.

CASSIRER, E. (1953a). *The Philosophy of Symbolic Forms*, Vol. 1 — Language. Yale University Press.

CASSIRER, E. (1953b). *The Philosophy of Symbolic Forms*, Vol. III — The Phenomenology of Knowledge. Yale University Press.

CHOMSKY, N. (1968). 'Linguistic Contributions to the Study of Mind Future', in *Language and Mind*, pp. 58–85. New York: Harcourt, Brace and World.

DEPARTMENT OF EDUCATION AND SCIENCE (1968). (Lewis Report) *The Education of Deaf Children*. London: H.M.S.O.

FRASER, C., BELLUGI, A. and BROWN, R. (1963). 'Control of Grammar in Imitation, Comprehension and Production', in OLDFIELD, R. C. and MARSHALL, J. C. (Eds.) *Language*, pp. 48–69. Harmondsworth: Penguin.

FURTH, H. C. (1969). *Piaget and Knowledge: Theoretical Foundations*. Englewood Cliffs, N. J.: Prentice Hall.

LEA, J. (1970). *The Colour Pattern Scheme. A Method of Remedial Language Teaching*. Moor House School, Hurst Green, Oxted, Surrey.

LENNEBERG, E. H. (1964). 'A Biological Perspective of Language', in OLDFIELD, R. C. and MARSHALL, J. C. (Eds.) *Language*, pp. 32–47. Harmondsworth: Penguin.

LEVINE, E. S. (1956). *Youth in a Soundless World:* New York University Press. *Search for Personality*.

MCGINNIS, KLEFFNER and GOLDSTEIN (1956). *Teaching Aphasic Children*. Reprint no. 677, The Volta Bureau.

PIAGET, J. (1968). *The Child s Construction of Reality*. London: Routledge and Kegan Paul.

PICKLES, D. G. (1966). 'The WISC Performance Scale and its Relationship to Speech and Educational Response in Deaf Slow Learning Children', *Teacher of the Deaf*, 64, 382–392.

SAPIR, E. (1921). *Language. An Introduction to the Study of Speech.* New York: Harcourt, Brace and World.

SINCLAIR DE ZWART, H. (1969). 'A Possible Theory of Language Acquisition within the General Framework of Piaget's Developmental Theory', in ADAMS, P. (Ed.) *Language in Thinking.* Harmondsworth: Penguin.

TERVOORT, F. (1964). 'The Effectiveness of Communication Among Deaf Children as a Contribution to Mental Growth', in EWING, A. (Ed.) *The Modern Educational Treatment of Deafness.* Manchester University Press.

VAN ZYL, F. J. and IVES, L. A. (1970). 'A Frostig DVP Study of Deaf Children Aged 6–8 years', *Teacher of the Deaf*, 68, 403.

VON HUMBOLDT, W. 'Über die Verschredenheit des Menschlichen Sprachbaues' ('Vorstudie zur Eileitung zum Kawi-Werk'), Werke, Gesammelte Schriften (Ekademie Ed.) 6, No. 1, 125s.s.

WOODWARD, M. (1971). *The Development of Behaviour.* Harmondsworth: Penguin.